How Do Penguins Play?

By **DIANE MULDROW**

Illustrated by **DAVID WALKER**

A GOLDEN BOOK • NEW YORK

rhcbooks.com
Educators and librarians, for a variety of teaching tools, visit us at
RHTeachersLibrarians.com
Distributed by: DOLGENCORP, LLC 100 Mission Ridge, Goodlettsville, TN 37072-2170
Spirit Marketing, LLC
706 Broadway, Suite 101, Kansas City, MO 64105
www.hellospiritmarketing.com
MANUFACTURED IN SHENZHEN, CHINA
ISBN 978-0-375-97801-2
05/18 – 06/18
DOLGEN21615301H18
10 9 8 7 6 5 4 3 2 1

Penguins like playing king of the hill!

Parrots will play
with a tweak on the bill.

Crows play
with sticks as
they fly through
the air . . .

and slide on their backs
in the snow, if they dare!

Breaching's big fun
for the humpback whale.

A woodpecker's toy
is another one's tail.

Dolphins blow bubbles,
then bounce them around.

Grizzly cubs wrestle
their friends to the ground.

Monkeys flip . . .

and seals flop.

Kangaroos like to box
as they hop.

Young goats leap high
and kick up their heels!

Sea otters are allowed
to play with their meals!

Cheetahs pounce the whole day through.

Animals love to play—just like you!